Write a word or number to finish each sentence.

_____

1. My name is _____.
   _____

2. I am _____ years old.
   _____

3. I have _____ brother(s).
   _____

4. I have _____ sister(s).
   _____

5. I can _____ this book!

Draw a picture of your family.

Look at the picture. Write how many you see.

1. swing sets

2. seesaws

3. slides

4. benches

Circle the one that has more.

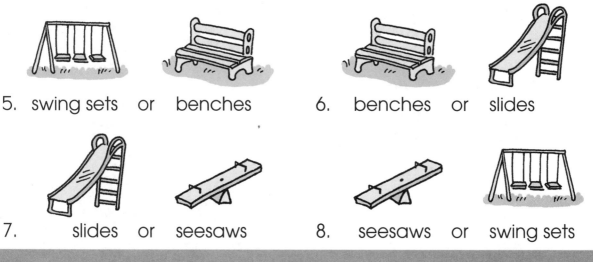

5. swing sets or benches

6. benches or slides

7. slides or seesaws

8. seesaws or swing sets

Read the rhyme.

> A-B-C-D-E-F-G
> Letters make the words I see.
>
> H-I-J-K Yes, indeed!
> I love letters. Can't you see?
>
> Skip, jump. L-M-N-O-P
> Q-R-S and T-U-V
>
> W and X and Y and Z
> ABCs are fun for me!

Circle the correct answers.

1. What is the poem about?

   seeing the sun   the alphabet

2. What is another good name for the poem?

   Letter Fun   Happy Birthday

3. What makes the words we see?

   letters   me

4. What is the alphabet for me?

   easy   fun

Read the story.

> Cookie is a cat.
> Cookie likes to cook.
> Cookie cooks cake.
> He cooks it from fish.
> Cookie cooks pie from fish, too.
> Cookie even cooks cookies from fish!

Circle the correct answers.

1. What is the best name for the story?

   A Real Cat   A Cat That Cooks

2. What does Cookie use to make everything he cooks?

   fish   cake

3. What kind of animal is Cookie?

   a real cat   a make-believe cat

Which sentences are correct? Circle **yes** or **no**.

4. Real cats can cook.   yes   no

5. Real cats can eat fish.   yes   no

6. Cookie is a real cat.   yes   no

4

Read the invitation.

Come to a party!

What:
Jenny's birthday party

Where:
Jenny's house

Date:
May 5

Time:
2:00 p.m.

Circle the correct answers.

1. Who is having the party?   Jenny   birthday

2. What is the party for?   birthday   house

3. Where will the party be?   park   house

4. What day is the party?   May 5   2:00 p.m.

5. What time is the party?   2:00 p.m.   May 5

Answer the question.

6. What will you take to the party?

I will take _____

Read the picture story.

Do you want a dog? Go to a pet store. Pick out a dog.

Take your dog home.

What will you name your dog?

Show how to buy a pet.
Number the pictures from **1** to **4** to show the correct order.

Pick out a pet.

Take your pet home.

Go to a pet store.

Name your pet.

Read the story.

> The night was dark.
> Tina heard something go "whooo!"
> Tina was scared.
>
> The window blew open.
> Tina saw an owl.
> The owl went "whooo!"
> Tina was not scared then.

Circle the correct answers.

1. What is the story about?

   how owls live   a scary night

2. What is the best name for the story?

   A Scary Sound   Tina's Pet

3. What did Tina hear?

   a ghost   an owl

4. Number the sentences from **1** to **4** to show the correct order.

   _____ The window blew open.

   _____ Tina was scared.

   _____ Tina saw an owl.

   _____ Tina was not scared then.

Read the note.

Mom,
I am outside. I went to the park. Adam is with me. We will be home by noon.
I love you,
Erica

Circle the correct answers.

1. What kind of writing is this?

   a sign   a note

2. Did Mom write the note?   yes   no

3. Is this note to Adam?   yes   no

4. Is Erica going to the park?   yes   no

5. Will Erica be home by noon?   yes   no

6. Who do you think Adam is?

   Erica's friend   Erica's teacher

SHOES!

Draw lines from the sentences to the correct shoes.

1. These are pink.

2. These have laces.

3. These are purple.

---

4. These are for skating.

5. These are for babies.

6. These are for snow.

---

7. These are for clowns.

8. These warm your toes!

Cross out the one that **does not belong**.

1.

2.

3.

4.

5.

6.

10

Read the story.

> There are many kinds of apples.
> Apples are red, green, and yellow.
> All apples grow on trees.
> Some apples are sweet.
> Sweet apples taste good raw.
> Other apples are tart.
> Tart apples taste best cooked.

Circle the correct answers.

1. What is the story about?

   sweet things   apples

2. What colors are apples?

   red, green, yellow   red, blue, yellow

3. What does **tart** mean?

   sweet   sour

4. Which apples taste better cooked?

   tart apples   red apples

5. Which kinds of apples have you eaten?
   Circle each kind you have tried.

Read the story.

Kids can do many jobs.
They can rake leaves.
They can sweep sidewalks.
They can help carry packages.

Kids are not ready to do some jobs.
They cannot drive buses.
They cannot drive dump trucks.

Circle the correct answers.

1. What is the best name for the story?

   Jobs for Kids   Kids Are Too Little

2. What is a job that kids can do?

   drive buses   sweep sidewalks

3. What is a job that kids cannot do?

   rake leaves   drive cars

Answer the question.

What work will you do when you grow up?

_____

_____

_____

Draw what happens **next**.

1. It is time to cool off.

2. It is time to play.

3. It is time for lunch.

4. The sun gets hot.

Words that rhyme sound the same at the end.
Pan and **can** rhyme. **Mike** and **bike** rhyme.

Circle the words that rhyme.

1.

dog   log   bird   hog

2.

man   pin   fan   can

3.

boy   boat   coat   goat

4.

two   shoe   blue   bow

MAKING A SANDWICH

Read how to make a sandwich.

Ham and Cheese Sandwich Recipe

What you need: two pieces of bread, some ham, some cheese

1. Get two pieces of bread.
2. Put some ham on one piece.
3. Put some cheese on the ham.
4. Put the other slice of bread on top.
5. Eat!

Show how to make a sandwich.
Number the pictures from **1** to **4** to show the correct order.

Read the picture story.

Amy got on the bus.

It was her first bus ride ever.

The driver showed Amy her seat.

The bus stopped many times.

Other kids got on.

Where was the bus going?

Circle the correct answers.

1. What did Amy get on?   bus   boat

2. Who showed Amy where to sit?   mother   driver

3. Who got on when the bus stopped?   dogs   kids

4. Did Amy ride the bus before?   yes   no

5. Did the bus stop a lot?   yes   no

Answer the question.

6. Where was the bus going?

_____

Help put the crayons away. Follow the directions.

Make a **red** line to put the **red** crayon away.
Make a yellow line to put the yellow crayon away.
Make a **blue** line to put the **blue** crayon away.
Make a green line to put the green crayon away.

Finish the sentence by writing the name of your favorite color.

My favorite color is

PEANUT BUTTER

Read the story.

You can eat peanut butter on bread. You can eat it on crackers. You can eat it with jam. I like to eat it on apples.

Peanut butter is made from peanuts and oil. The peanuts are ground up. Then you add a little oil. Now you have peanut butter.

Answer the questions.

1. What can we eat with peanut butter?

_____   _____

_____   _____

_____   _____

_____   _____

2. What is peanut butter made from?

_____   _____

_____ and _____

3. Do you like to eat peanut butter?

_____

_____

1. Draw one more thing that belongs in each group.

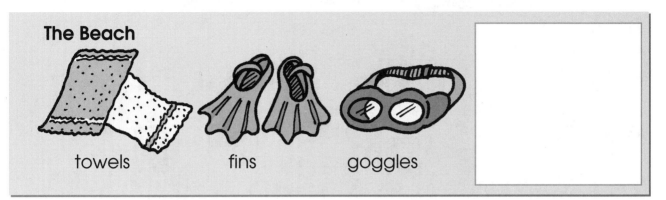

The Beach

towels　　　fins　　　goggles

A Picnic

drinks　　　dishes　　　food

2. Use two words from above to write a riddle.
   Read your riddle to a friend.

I am going somewhere. I will take some

_____ and

_____

some _____ . Where am I going?

_____

I am going _____ .

Color the boxes to show how many there are.

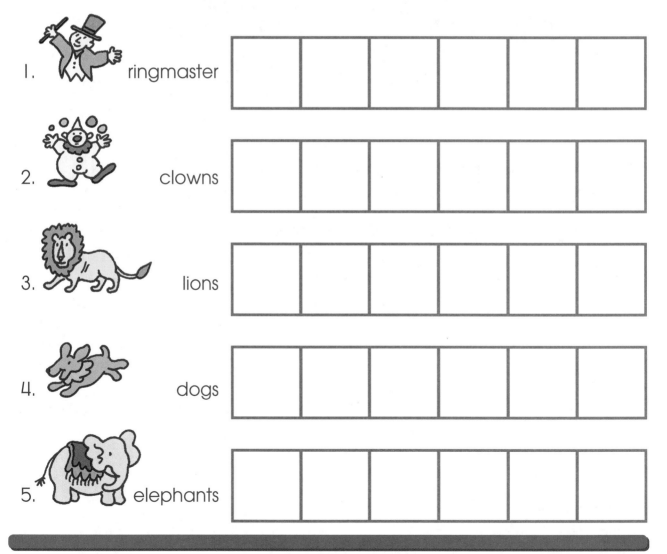

1. ringmaster

2. clowns

3. lions

4. dogs

5. elephants

LEAVES

Read the story.

The wind was blowing.
Leaves fell from the trees.
Many leaves were red,
orange, and yellow.
Ty found a red leaf.
Which season was it?

Circle the correct answers.

1. What is another good name for the story?

   Winter   The Red Leaf

2. Which picture shows the weather that day?

3. What did Ty find?

4. Which season was it?

   spring   summer   fall   winter

Read the story.

> Hal did not like being an alien.
> He wanted to be a kid.
> He left his planet.
> He went to Earth.
>
> Hal saw a doll.
> He thought it was a kid.
> The doll did not talk.
> It was not fun, so Hal
> went back home.

Circle the correct answers.

1. What is the story about?

    a doll   an alien

2. What is an **alien**?

    someone from another planet

    a kid who wants to be a doll

3. What did Hal want to be?

    a doll   a kid

4. Which one is Hal?

Read the story.

> The monsters had a party.
> They played monster games.
> They did monster dances.
> Then they cleaned up.
>
> Monster Mom said, "Monsters are messy. Mess this room up, right now!"

Circle the correct answers.

1. Which one is a monster?

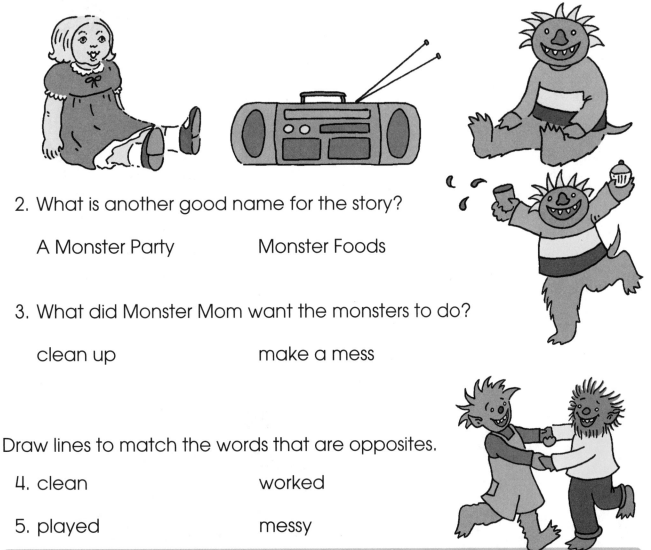

2. What is another good name for the story?

   A Monster Party   Monster Foods

3. What did Monster Mom want the monsters to do?

   clean up   make a mess

Draw lines to match the words that are opposites.

4. clean   worked

5. played   messy

Read the story.

> Our team is the best.
> Our team never rests.
>
> Our team really hits.
> Our team never quits.
>
> Before the games begin,
> We know that we will win!

Circle the correct answers.

1. What is the poem about?

   our baseball team   our school

2. What is a team?

   a group that works together   a person who works

3. Which word finishes the sentence?
   "Our team never _____."

   quits   loses

4. Which word rhymes with **quits**?

   hits   rests

Color the squares to show how many there are.

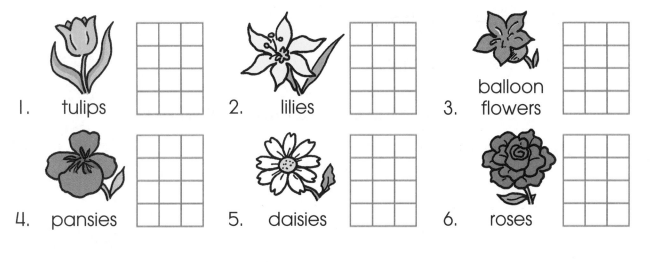

1. tulips

2. lilies

3. balloon flowers

4. pansies

5. daisies

6. roses

Check the boxes to answer the questions.

7. Which has the most?

8. Which has the fewest?

9. Which has the same number as the tulips?

☐ tulips   ☐ roses

☐ daisies   ☐ balloon flowers

☐ pansies   ☐ lilies

Answer the question.

Which flower do you like best?

_____

I like the _____ best.

Read about book covers.

A book cover tells the name of a book.
It tells who wrote the book.
It tells who drew the pictures.

1. Check the things that a book cover tells.

☐ who wrote the book

☐ when the book was made

☐ the name of the book

☐ who drew the pictures

Answer the questions about the cover shown on this page.

2. Who wrote this book?

_____

_____

3. Who drew the pictures?

_____

_____

4. What is this book about?

_____

_____

Read the story.

When Zach woke up,
no one was home.
Where was his family?
Zach heard a barking sound.
What was it?

Zach found his family
in the backyard.
"Happy Birthday!" they said.
They were playing with
Zach's new puppy.

Circle the correct answers.

1. What is the best name for the story?

   Zach's Surprise   The Family Car

2. What did Zach hear?

   a laugh   barking

Draw lines to match the parts of the sentences.

3. When Zach woke up,   no one was home.

4. "Happy Birthday!"   with Zach's new puppy.

5. They were playing   they said.

Read the note.

Dear Grandma,

You sent such a nice surprise!

Thank you for my new skates.

They will look great with my new helmet.

I love you,
Maria

Circle the correct answers.

1. What kind of writing is this?

   a note   a birthday card

2. Who wrote it?

   Maria   Grandma

3. Who is it for?

   Grandma   Maria

4. What will Maria wear with her skates?

WHAT DO YOU KNOW?

Read the clues.
Write the answers in the puzzle.

| cold | dry | new | open | closed | hot | wet | old |

Across

1. No one is in the school.
   The school is _____.

5. I got these shoes long ago.
   These shoes are _____.

6. Mom just bought a car.
   The car is _____.

Down

1. It is snowing outside.
   It is _____.

2. People are shopping.
   The store is _____.

3. I wiped water off the floor.
   The floor is now _____.

4. Dinner is cooking in the oven.
   The oven is _____.

7. The dog was out in the rain.
   The dog is _____.

Drawing Conclusions/Opposites

Read the clues.
Write the names under the correct pictures.

Sara has a green hat.

Mia always wears red.

Kenji has a puppy.

Mimi likes to paint.

Ty has purple shoes.

Bob likes to wear blue.

1.

_____

_____

2.

_____

_____

3.

_____

_____

4.

_____

5.

_____

6.

_____

30

Read the riddle.

> You see me at the beach.
> You see me in a game.
> I am round and filled with air.
> I can be many colors.
> What am I?

Circle the correct answers.

1. What kind of writing is this?

   a note   a riddle

2. What is the best name for the riddle?

   What Am I?   Games and Work

3. What is the riddle about?

   a beach ball   a float

Which sentences are correct?
Circle **yes** or **no**.

4. It is filled with air.   yes   no

5. It is always red.   yes   no

6. It is round.   yes   no

Read the story.

> Willie was a little car.
> Everyone called him "The Bug."
> Willie couldn't go fast, but he was always ready.
>
> One day, the family had a problem.
> They got in their fast car, but it didn't go.
>
> Willie was ready. Willie saved the day!

Circle the correct answers.

1. What is the story about?

   a family   a car

2. What is the best name for the story?

   Fast Cars Are Best   Willie Saves the Day

3. What was it that Willie could not do?

   go slow   go fast

4. Which one is Willie?

Draw lines from the sentences to the correct hats.

1. Wear a tall hat to cook.

2. Wear this hat to the game.

3. Wear a helmet to ride.

4. Wear a hat with a name.

5. Wear a hat that is soft.

6. Wear a gray hat.

7. Wear a hat made of straw.

8. Wear a Happy Birthday hat!

Circle the animals that look real.

THE DANCE

Read the story.

It would be the best dance!
Every dinosaur was coming.
Deeny wanted to be cool.
He got out his cool dino shoes.

Uh-oh! One shoe has a hole.
Deeny filled the hole with gum.
When the music began,
Deeny stuck to the floor!
Deeny took off his shoes.
He was cool anyway.

Circle the correct answers.

1. What is another good name for the story?

   Real Dinosaurs   Deeny's Dino Shoes

2. What did Deeny put in his shoe?

   gum   a hole

3. What happened then?

   Deeny stuck to the floor.   Deeny fell down.

4. Which one is Deeny?

Read the poem.

There was an old woman
who lived in a boot.
She fed all her children
crackers and fruit.

When nighttime would come,
she'd say, "Off to bed! Scoot!"
And she'd play them to sleep
with a song from her flute.

Circle the correct answers.

1. What is the poem about?

   boots   an ant family

2. What does **scoot** mean?

   go quickly   go slowly

3. What does the woman make with her flute?

   boots   music

4. Which pictures have names that rhyme with **scoot**?

Read the directions.

To play Toss the Penny, you need ten pennies and a muffin tin.

Put the tin near a wall.
Stand about ten steps away.
Toss a penny. Try to get it in a hole.
How many pennies can you get in?

Circle the correct answers.

1. Where should you put the muffin tin?

   near a wall   under a bed

2. Where should you stand?

   5 steps away   10 steps away

3. What should you do with the penny?

   toss it   spin it

4. Where do you want the penny to go?

   in your pocket   in a hole

5. Circle how many pennies you need to play this game.

Read the story.

> I know a silly man
> who walks on his hands.
> He has a silly car,
> but it doesn't go too far.
> In his silly town,
> shops are upside down.
> Tell me, if you can,
> when you see this silly man.

Circle the correct answers.

1. Which one is the silly man?

2. Which car is his?

3. Which hat is his?

4. Which pet is his?

Read about uniforms.

> Some clothes are uniforms.
> Uniforms are special clothes.
> They tell about people's jobs.
> What kinds of uniforms have
> you seen?

Circle the correct answers.

1. What is the story about?

   people   uniforms

2. What are uniforms?

   special people   special clothes

3. Which one is a uniform?

4. What do uniforms tell us?

   a person's job   someone's address

Read the story.

> In Alaska, dogs pull sleds over the snow. Dogsleds are better than cars in deep snow.
>
> Dogs also help people who cannot see. The dogs lead the way and help the owners know where to go.
>
> Have you seen a working dog?

Circle the correct answers.

1. What is the story about?

   pet dogs   working dogs

2. What work do some dogs do?

   drive cars   pull sleds

3. What other work do some dogs do?

   help people who cannot see   help people sleep

4. Do dogs pull sleds?   yes   no

5. Do dogs drive cars?   yes   no

6. Do dogs help people?   yes   no

1. Follow the directions.
   Then read the words that are left.

   Color the **Y** boxes **red**.

   Color the **C** boxes **blue**.

   Color the **J** boxes orange.

   Color the **H** boxes **purple**.

   Color the **Z** boxes green.

Y	I	C	J	Z	L	I	K	E	C
R	E	D	C	J	Z	Y	H	J	Y
H	Z	Y	F	L	O	W	E	R	S
A	N	D	Y	P	U	R	P	L	E
C	J	B	A	L	L	O	O	N	S.

2. Write the words. Show the message to someone.

_____

_____

_____

_____

OPPOSITES PUZZLE

Read the clues.
Write opposites in the puzzle.

cold	down	go	left	lost	out

Across

1. found
3. hot
5. in

Down

1. right
2. stop
4. up

GIRAFFE STORY

Read the story.

Giraffe likes to draw and dance.
She thought she should do just
one. Giraffe got dancing shoes.
She danced every day.

Giraffe went to the tryout for
the dance group, but she was
too tall for the stage!

At first, Giraffe was sad. Then she
had a good idea! She would
draw dancers. Then she would be
part of both things she likes!

Circle the correct answers.

1. Did Giraffe want to be a dancer?   yes   no

2. Did Giraffe get dancing shoes?   yes   no

3. Did Giraffe go to Dancing School?   yes   no

4. What do you find out at a tryout?

   if you can join   if you are too smart

5. What is a good name for the story?

   Drawing   Dancing   Giraffe's Idea

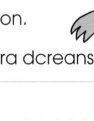

Unscramble the words to answer the question.

6. What was Giraffe's good idea?   dwra dcreans

Giraffe would _____.

Read the note.

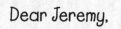

Dear Jeremy,

We are having a party on July 4th.
There will be a picnic at 6:00.
Bring foods you like to eat.
We can watch fireworks!
Will you come?

Tyrone

Circle the correct answers.

1. What kind of writing is this?

   an invitation   a song

2. What kind of party is it?

   a picnic   a birthday party

3. What should Jeremy bring?

   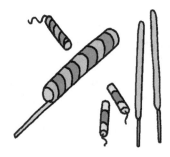   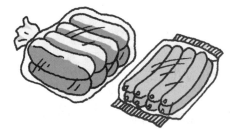

4. Is the party for Thanksgiving?   yes   no

5. Is the party for the Fourth of July?   yes   no

6. Will the picnic start at 6:00?   yes   no

7. Will there be food at the party?   yes   no

Sid gave Lars a note at school.
The note was in code.

12-5-20-19 16-12-1-25 19-16-25.

3-15-13-5 15-22-5-18

1-6-20-5-18 19-3-8-15-15-12.

Help Lars break the code.

I	2	3	4	5	6	7	8	9	10	11	12	13	14	15	16	17	18	19	20	21	22	23	24	25	26
A	B	C	D	E	F	G	H	I	J	K	L	M	N	O	P	Q	R	S	T	U	V	W	X	Y	Z

Write the correct letters in the boxes.
Then read the message.

12 5 20 19

16 12 1 25

19 16 25

3 15 13 5

15 22 5 18

1 6 20 5 18

19 3 8 15 15 12

Read the story.

Do you put things away?
That makes them easy to find later.

Lisa puts her toys away.
She puts the art things in the art box.
She puts toys in the toy box.
She puts books on the bookshelf.

Draw lines from the things to where they go.

Read the story.

Friends are people who care about you.
They want you to be happy.
They like to be with you.
Friends are special people.
Friends make the world a better place.

Circle the correct answers.

1. What is the story about?

   feelings   friends

2. What is one thing friends do?

   They go to school.   They care about you.

Draw lines to match the parts of the sentences.

3. Friends are people   be happy.

4. They want you to   special people.

5. They like to   who care about you.

6. Friends are   be with you.

7. Friends make the world   a better place.

Read the story.

Shh. You are in a library.
People read in the library,
so please be quiet.

When you are at the library,
you can pick out a book.
You can take the book home
to read it, but remember to
bring it back!

Circle the correct answers.

1. What is the story about?

   people   the library

2. What can you do at the library?

   pick out a book   watch a show

3. What should you remember to do with your book?

   bring it back   give it away

Number the sentences from **1** to **3** to show the correct order.

4. _____ Read the book at home.

   _____ Pick out a book.

   _____ Bring it back to the library.

MOUSE'S HOUSE

Read the story.

> Mouse needed a house.
> It did not have to be big or pretty.
> It had to be dry and warm because
> winter was coming.
>
> Mouse looked in a tree.
> It was not warm.
> Mouse looked under a leaf.
> It was not dry.
> Mouse found a boot.
> It was dry and warm.
> Mouse had a new home.

Circle the correct answers.

1. What is the story about?

   finding a house   Mouse's family

2. What did the house have to be?

   warm and dry   big and dry

3. Why did Mouse need a house?

   He was lost.   Winter was coming.

4. Which is Mouse's new house?

Read the poem.

Five little monkeys went to play
out in the park one sunny day.

When Uncle Baboon said,
"On your way!"
All the little monkeys said,
"Can we stay?"

Uncle Baboon said, "Oh, okay!
I do like to see my monkeys play."

Circle the correct answers.

1. What is a good name for the poem?

   Monkeys in the Park   The Mad Baboon

2. Who was the baboon?

   the monkeys' dad   the monkeys' uncle

3. Was only one monkey playing?   yes   no

4. Did the monkeys want to stay?   yes   no

5. Did the baboon let them stay?   yes   no

Main Idea/Details   **50**   © School Zone Publishing Company 02241

Draw lines to things that are almost the same, but **bigger**.

1.

2.

3.

4.

5.

6.

Comparing/Classifying

Draw lines from the sentences to the correct pictures.

1. This tool is for digging.

2. This tool is for writing.

3. These tools are for eating.

4. This is for firefighting.

5. These are for running.

6. This is for mailing.

7. This is for the dark.

8. This takes you sailing.

Read the story.

A stranger walked into the barn.
He was wearing a long coat and a hat.
He had hair on his chin. He did not talk.
Who was he?

Cow was afraid. Horse was afraid.
Rat went to take a closer look.
The stranger's legs were hairy.
He had a tail. It was just Goat.
Goat was playing a trick!

Circle the correct answers.

1. What is the best name for the story?

   The Animals   Stranger in the Barn

2. What did the stranger wear?

   a hat and pants   a hat and a coat

3. Who was wearing the coat?

   Horse   Goat

4. What was Goat doing?

   playing a trick   trying to hide

SID SNAKE

Read the story.

> Sid Snake makes shapes.
> Sid makes a circle when he sees the sun. Sid makes an S when someone asks his name. Sid makes an egg when he sees a bird.
>
> Sid is so curvy that he cannot make a triangle. He cannot make a square.

Circle the correct answers.

1. What is the best name for the story?

   Real Snakes   Sid's Shapes

2. What shape did Sid make?

   circle   square

3. Can Sid make a triangle?   yes   no

4. Can Sid make an **S**?   yes   no

Draw a picture of Sid in the box.

WORD PUZZLE

Unscramble the clues.
Write the words in the puzzle.

| blue | boat | drum | into | mine | tree |

Across

1. lbeu
3. mudr
5. iton

Down

1. oatb
2. eret
4. nmie

WRITING A STORY

Finish the story. Use List A or List B.
Read your story to a friend.

List A

store   dad   a book   people

List B

circus   mom   a balloon   clowns

Today, I will go to the _____ .

_____

My _____ will go with me.

_____

It will be fun! I will buy _____ .

_____

I will see _____ .

I will read the words I see!

Read the story.

> Jess got dressed.
> She ate her breakfast.
> She kissed her mom and
> walked to school.
>
> No one was there!
> The rooms were empty.
> The doors were locked.
> "Oh, no! It's Saturday!" Jess said.

Circle the correct answers.

1. What is the best name for the story?

   Jess Goes to School   Go to the Store

2. What day was it?

   Monday   Saturday

3. Where did Jess go?

   to school   to the park

4. How did Jess get there?

57

Read the sign.

Welcome to the Park!
The park is open from
9:00 a.m. to 5:00 p.m.

Come to the show!
Shows are at 10:00 a.m. and 2:00 p.m.

Rules:
Do not feed the animals.
Do not litter.
Do not pick the wildflowers.
DO HAVE FUN!

Circle the correct answers.

1. What kind of writing is this?

   a sign   a book

2. Where would you find this?

   a school   in the park

3. When do the shows start?

   10:00 a.m. and 9:00 p.m.   10:00 a.m. and 2:00 p.m.

4. What is okay to do at the park?

Read the story.

> This is our American flag.
> Some people call our flag
> "The Stars and Stripes."
> Our flag is red, white, and blue.
> The flag has 13 stripes.
> Seven are red. Six are white.
> There are 50 stars. There is one
> star for each state in our country.

Circle the correct answers.

1. What is the story about?

   the American flag   stripes

2. What color are the stripes?

   red and blue   red and white

3. How many red stripes are there?
   How many white stripes are there?

   50 red, 13 white   7 red, 6 white

Answer the question.

4. Why are there 50 stars?

_____

_____

_____

THE ARTIST

Read the story.

> Pete is an artist, but everything
> Pete draws looks like Pete.
>
> Pete painted a house.
> It was big, tan, and furry.
> Pete painted the door.
> It had sharp teeth.
> Pete painted a garden.
> The flowers looked like claws.
> Silly Pete!

Circle the correct answers.

1. What is the best name for the story?

   Pete's Garden   Pete, the Artist

2. Is Pete a person?   yes   no

3. Is Pete a bear?   yes   no

4. Does Pete have claws?   yes   no

Draw a picture that Pete might draw.

ANSWER KEY

Page 1
1. (name)
2. (age)
3. (# of brothers)
4. (# of sisters)
5. read
Picture should show family.

Page 2
1. 2 swing sets
3. 2 slides
5. benches
7. seesaws
2. 3 seesaws
4. 3 benches
6. benches
8. seesaws

Page 3
1. the alphabet
2. Letter Fun
3. letters
4. fun

Page 4
1. A Cat That Cooks
2. fish
3. a make-believe cat
4. no
5. yes
6. no

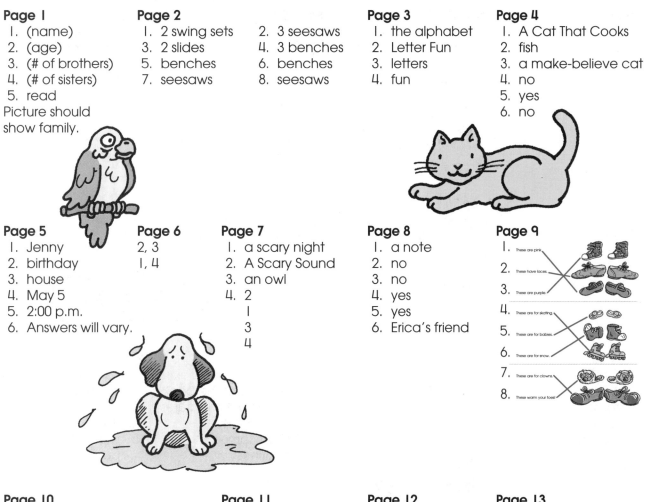

Page 5
1. Jenny
2. birthday
3. house
4. May 5
5. 2:00 p.m.
6. Answers will vary.

Page 6
2, 3
1, 4

Page 7
1. a scary night
2. A Scary Sound
3. an owl
4. 2
   1
   3
   4

Page 8
1. a note
2. no
3. no
4. yes
5. yes
6. Erica's friend

Page 9
1. These are pink.
2. These have laces.
3. These are purple.
4. These are for skating.
5. These are for babies.
6. These are for snow.
7. These are for clowns.
8. These warm your toes!

Page 10
1. wagon
3. ring
5. cake
2. car
4. swimsuit
6. blue jeans

Page 11
1. apples
2. red, green, yellow
3. sour
4. tart apples
5. Answers will vary.

Page 12
1. Jobs for Kids
2. sweep sidewalks
3. drive cars
Answers will vary.

Page 13
1. child swimming
2. child skating
3. child eating
4. snowman melted

Page 14

Page 15
4, 1
3, 2

Page 16
1. bus
2. driver
3. kids
4. no
5. yes
6. school

Page 17

Answers will vary.

ANSWER KEY

Page 18
1. bread, crackers, jam, apples
2. peanuts, oil
3. Answers will vary.

Page 19
1. Child should have added appropriate pictures.
2. Answers should be words from one of the groups above. Last answer should fit the chosen items.

Page 20

1.
2.
3.
4.
5.

Page 21
1. The Red Leaf
2. windy picture
3. red leaf picture
4. fall

Page 22
1. an alien
2. someone from another planet
3. a kid
4. alien picture

Page 23
1. monster picture
2. A Monster Party
3. make a mess
4. messy
5. worked

Page 24
1. our baseball team
2. a group that works together
3. quits
4. hits

Page 25
1. 6 tulips   2. 8 lilies   3. 7 balloon flowers
4. 6 pansies   5. 5 daisies   6. 11 roses
7. roses
8. daisies
9. pansies
Answers will vary.

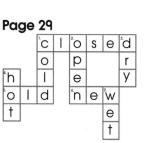

Page 26
1. who wrote the book
   the name of the book
   who drew the pictures
2. Tyrone James
3. Robert James
4. valentines

Page 27
1. Zach's Surprise
2. a sound
3. no one was home.
4. they said.
5. with Zach's new puppy.

Page 28
1. a note
2. Maria
3. Grandma
4. helmet picture

Page 29

	c	l	o	s	e	d
	o		p			r
	l		e			y
h	o	l	d		n	e	w
	t					e
						t

Page 30
1. Sara   2. Kenji   3. Mia
4. Ty   5. Mimi   6. Bob

Page 31
1. a riddle
2. What Am I?
3. a beach ball
4. yes
5. no
6. yes

Page 32
1. a car
2. Willie Saves the Day
3. go fast
4. yellow car picture

Page 33
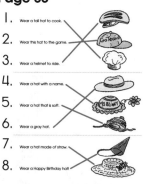
1. Wear a tall hat to cook.
2. Wear this hat to the game.
3. Wear a helmet to ride.
4. Wear a hat with a name.
5. Wear a hat that is soft.
6. Wear a gray hat.
7. Wear a hat made of straw.
8. Wear a Happy Birthday hat!

Page 34
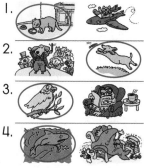
1.
2.
3.
4.

62

ANSWER KEY

Page 35
1. Deeny's Dino Shoes
2. gum
3. Deeny stuck to the floor.
4. orange dinosaur picture

Page 36
1. an ant family
2. go quickly
3. music
4. boot picture and fruit picture

Page 37
1. near a wall
2. 10 steps away
3. toss it
4. in a hole
5.

Page 38
1.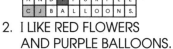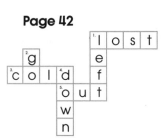
2.
3.
4.

Page 39
1. uniforms
2. special clothes
3. uniform picture
4. a person's job

Page 40
1. working dogs
2. pull sleds
3. help people who cannot see
4. yes
5. no
6. yes

Page 41
1.
```
Y I C J Z L I K E C
R E D C J Z Y H J Y
H Z Y F L O W E R S
A N D Y P U R P L E
C J B A L L O O N S
```
2. I LIKE RED FLOWERS AND PURPLE BALLOONS.

Page 42
```
        l o s t
        e
  g     f
c o l d
    o u t
    w
    n
```

Page 43
1. yes
2. yes
3. no
4. if you can join
5. Giraffe's Idea
6. draw dancers

Page 44
1. an invitation
2. a picnic
3. food picture
4. no
5. yes
6. yes
7. yes

Page 45
LET'S PLAY SPY.
COME OVER
AFTER SCHOOL.

Page 46

Page 47
1. friends
2. They care about you.
3. who care about you.
4. be happy.
5. be with you.
6. special people.
7. a better place.

Page 48
1. the library
2. pick out a book
3. bring it back
4. 2
   1
   3

Page 49
1. finding a house
2. warm and dry
3. Winter was coming.
4. boot picture

Page 50
1. Monkeys in the Park
2. the monkeys' uncle
3. no
4. yes
5. yes

ANSWER KEY

Page 51

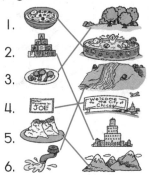

1.
2.
3.
4.
5.
6.

Accept other answers that your child can support.

Page 52

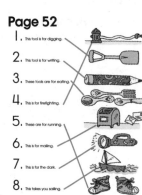

1. This tool is for digging.
2. This tool is for writing.
3. These tools are for eating.
4. This is for firefighting.
5. These are for running.
6. This is for mailing.
7. This is for the dark.
8. This takes you sailing.

Page 53

1. Stranger in the Barn
2. a hat and a coat
3. Goat
4. playing a trick

Page 54

1. Sid's Shapes
2. circle
3. no
4. yes

Picture should show a snake.

Page 55

		b	l	u	e
	t		o		
d	r	u	m	a	
	e		i	n	t	o
	e		n		
			e		

Page 56

Story should include words from List A or List B.

Page 57

1. Jess Goes to School
2. Saturday
3. to school
4. girl picture

Page 58

1. a sign
2. in the park
3. 10:00 a.m. and 2:00 p.m.
4. people playing ball picture

Page 59

1. the American flag
2. red and white
3. 7 red, 6 white
4. There is one star for each state.

Page 60

1. Pete, the Artist
2. no
3. yes
4. yes

Picture should include bear attributes.